C000295999

The Story of
Ribblehead Viaduct

A RARE VIEW OF RIBBLEHEAD

In the autumn of 1989, as remedial work was undertaken, the line was closed for a fortnight, the tracks were taken up and the old ballast removed as a prelude to making the deck good and to providing a waterproof membrane.

Above: Replacing faulty brickwork under one of the high arches.

Opposite page, below: A group of engineers beside one of the scaffolded piers.

The Story of Ribblehead Viaduct

(Revised edition)

Text: W. R. Mitchell

Visuals: Peter Fox

Pictured above is James Allport, the Midland Railway's general manager, who was perturbed by the conditions the Midland had to tolerate when sending its passengers and goods along the London and North Western, to Scotland. He was the inspiration behind an alternative route: the Settle-Carlisle Railway.

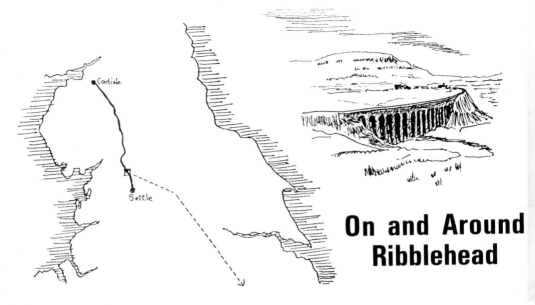

On and Around Ribblehead

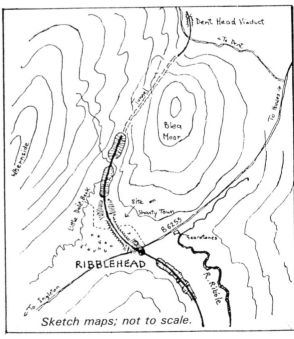

Sketch maps; not to scale.

Printed by Lamberts Print & Design, Station Road, Settle, North Yorkshire, BD24 9AA.
Published by W.R. Mitchell, 18 Yealand Avenue, Giggleswick, Settle, North Yorkshire, BD24 0AY.

© W.R. Mitchell, 1990. Revised edition 2001.

ISBN: 1 871064 08 2.

Contents

Illustrations:

Front cover, top – The Tasmanian engineer John Sharland, who worked out a practical route the Settle-Carlisle could take. *Below* – The first steam passenger train to cross Ribblehead Viaduct after the 1989 water-proofing at Ribblehead *(Peter Fox)*.

Back cover, top – One of the first regular diesel-hauled trains to be accompanied by specially requested loco-motives. In this case two Class 20s assist a Class 47 *(Peter Fox)*. *Below* – The crane used in 1989 *(W.R. Mitchell)*.

Sketch maps on page 4 by Peter Fox. *This page, above* – 46229, in March, 1983 *(Peter Fox)*.

Peter Fox: Uncredited line drawings. Photos – 5, 7, 8, 12, 19, 28, 30, 44-47.

British Rail: 1-4, 9, 15-17, 20, 26-27, 35, 38, 43, 47 (bottom).

The Yorkshire Post: 48.

George Horner: 13.

Simon Pawson: Aerial photograph, 24-25.

Rowland Lindup: Page 21 (top), 41 (bottom), 42 (top).

Dr J A Farrer: 10,13

North Craven Building Trust: Drawings by Betty Harrington – 18 *(top)*, 42 *(bottom)*.

P. Weston Collection: 44 *(bottom)*.

F.S. Williams The Midland Railway: 3 *(top)*, 40.

Foreword

by

A. P. Freschini

Photo: W R Mitchell

READING through this fine account of the history of the bridge, one continues to gain in respect and admiration for the men who built and maintained this great structure throughout the years in its inhospitable environment.

We present-day engineers like to consider ourselves hardy souls, yet how pampered we are today with our comfortable site offices, protective clothing and modern equipment, compared with our 1870 predecessors. Not for us the long hard day's work battling against the elements, followed by the spartan shanty town life.

I am sure all will be impressed by the magnitude of the original contract which included the major viaducts at Ribblehead and Denthead, Blea Moor Tunnel and 72 miles of railway—civil engineering on a grand scale! The complexities of managing a work of this size would be daunting even today. How difficult it must have been in the 1870s. The organisational skills used to direct men, materials and equipment efficiently throughout this large site must have been of excellent quality. It is a tribute to the Victorian engineers that so much good work was accomplished in such a short time.

Considering the bleak windswept nature of its location, Ribblehead has endured the ravages of the weather remarkably well. However, it has now become necessary to carry out some essential remedial works to secure its future as a working railway bridge for many years to come.

My first experience of working on this bridge occurred in 1988, when I was delighted to become Resident Engineer for the trial repair scheme. The primary purpose of the 1988 works was to establish how much it would cost to repair the complete structure. The trials were successful and the anticipated cost of the future works were found to be considerably less than expected, this fact, perhaps, contributing towards the removal of the line closure proposal.

The first phase of the major repairs were completed in 1989, when the bridge deck was waterproofed, an essential first measure to reduce the rate of deterioration of the whole bridge.

During the next few years it is intended to complete the repairs, restoring the structure to an acceptable condition.

Whatever else may have changed, the area seems to remain as windy as described in the past. Summer gales in 1988 caused an accumulated loss of 14 days working time out of our first 42 on site. I recall standing on the scaffold platform, 80ft above the ground, sheltering behind a pier, conscious only of the almost unbelievable roar of the wind rushing through the adjoining arches.

It is at such a time that one can visualise the original builders clinging to their timber trestles in the depths of a winter gale, yet having the grit and determination to surmount all obstacles and complete their great work.

I am sure that this national monument will endure and that its future will be as colourful and interesting as this description of its past.

Introduction

The viaduct when completed will be the admiration of all lovers of imposing and massive masonry, and no doubt generations unborn will look upon it with wonder and think how clever were their forefathers to rear such a structure.

THESE WORDS, by a newspaper writer of 1873, reflect the sense of wonder felt by many in north-west Yorkshire as Ribblehead Viaduct arose behind a "web" of wooden scaffolding. It was part of a bold Victorian scheme to drive a railway from Settle to Carlisle, using the north-south valleys of Ribblesdale and the Vale of Eden.

Some of the large Settle-Carlisle viaducts stand in the seclusion of narrow gills but Ribblehead is there for all to see—a stupendous feature on relatively flat ground, a feature backed up by Whernside which at 2,414 feet is itself a major feature of this wild Pennine landscape.

Originally known as Batty Wife Viaduct, after a fanciful story told about a natural shaft in the limestone, and now referred to prosaically as Bridge No. 66, Ribblehead Viaduct symbolises the strength, style and endurance of one of Britain's most famous railways.

The Settle-Carlisle was the Midland Company's bid to share the lucrative Scottish traffic; this was to be no ordinary "mountain railway" but one made as straight as possible and finely engineered so that it could carry crack expresses at all times of the day and in all kinds of weather on the 72 mile route extending from a junction with the Little North Western, one and a-half miles south of Settle, to Petteril Bridge Junction, on the outskirts of Carlisle. Every train enthusiast knows that the summit of the Settle-Carlisle at Aisgill is 1,169 feet above sea level.

Ribblesdale Viaduct has had to pay for its conspicuous situation in the Three Peaks Country. Westerly gales, funnelled by Chapel-le-Dale, howl on their way up the Dale and pass through the arches of the Viaduct with a noise like part of the soundtrack of a Brontë film. John Ruskin, the Victorian art critic, looking at Ingleborough on a windy day, wondered how the mountain managed to stand without rocking.

Ribblehead is one of the windiest places on earth, and one November gale produced gusts of over 100 miles an hour. In November, 1961, when Ribblehead station was also a weather-recording point, the anemometer noted 92 m.p.h. I chatted with a railway maintenance man who mentioned windy days when planks on the scaffolding erected on Ribblehead Viaduct went "up and down like piano keys".

I have been to Ribblehead when the wind has been so strong and rain so heavy I have stayed in the car. Once, as a thunderstorm raged, the sky was as dark as Stephen's Ink and forked lightning played around the

Viaduct as though intent on its destruction. There was another day when the Weather Clerk shook up a cocktail of varying circumstances, from snow falling diagonally to sunny intervals of such brilliance that I had to screw up my eyes to avoid distress. Ribblehead is a magical place when there is an autumn sunset and the familiar profile is silhouetted against an orange-red sky. Part of the appeal of this Victorian structure is the variation afforded by ordinary piers and every sixth, known as a king pier because it is twice the width.

This book deals with the conception, execution, maintenance and endurance of the stupendous viaduct. Up to 100 hardy masons and their helpers brought it into existence, using the plans of engineers of skill and confidence and quarrying limestone lifted from beds in Littledale and about Salt Lake. The viaduct was built in wetter-than-average Pennine weather.

The basic statistics are impressive — 23 piers (24 arches) with a width of 13 feet at the base and only six feet at the top; a span of 1,328 feet; a maximum height of 105 feet; 30,000 cubic yards of masonry and 6,000 of concrete. The parapet of the viaduct has base and coping stones of a yellowish gritstone which gives a nice contrast and are aesthetically very pleasing. Incidentally, it has also helped considerably in maintaining the strength of the structure.

Ribblehead Viaduct has stood for well over a century, defying the gods of the Pennine weather to disturb its ageing bones. The piers have a sure foundation. Shafts were driven for about 25 feet to bedrock, above which were laid six feet of concrete. Local people insist that Ribblehead Viaduct was "built on wool", yet the evidence that concrete was used is strong. Perhaps wool was used to stop the seepage of water into the shafts. Or could it have been that the Midland, ever short of money to finance their grandiose plans in those inflationary times, borrowed money from the Bradford Woolmen?

I have seen Ribblehead viaduct a thousand times, and cannot recall it looking the same on two separate occasions. In good weather, the shadow pattern gives it a distinctive appearance. The viaduct accentuates the natural contours and draws attention to the vastness of the landscape. Linear architecture which should look alien to this northern fell-country is now acceptable because it has been smoothed and weathered by the same natural forces — by wind, rain and frost — that are continually shaping the rocks round about.

Cumbrian Mountain Express crosses on the single track during viaduct repairs.

Ribblehead
before
the Railway

ON MANY days of the year there is an Ice Age chill about Ribblehead. Drumlins, heaps of rubble dating to the time when the glaciers melted, are a conspicuous feature of the district.

The Romans came this way, using a road they had made from Bainbridge, over Dodd Fell and Cam End to Gearstones and on to their Lune Valley road. The stretch of road descending from Cam End became known to local people as The Devil's Highway.

In the 18th century, a turnpike was made crossing those self-same "tops" but in due course to be re-routed through Hawes and Widdale. In 1792, the Hon. John Byng, later Lord Torringdon, travelling on horseback, reached Gearstones and shuddered. To Genial John, this plain building, this inn-cum-farmstead in a sodden, misty area was "the seat of misery in a desert."

Byng arrived as a cattle fair "added to the horror of the curious scenery." He saw beasts brought on the hoof from Scotland and now surrounded by drovers, buyers and sellers, many of whom wore plaids. Cattle men thronged the edge of the moor and also the little inn. Byng found there was no hay in the stable for his horse and that for dinner he was served boiled slices of stale pork and fried eggs, "with some wretched beer to which my hunger was not equal, and from which my delicacy revolted."

A clergyman traveller in 1818 used the family's horse-drawn coach from Lancaster; he noted that from about Weathercote Cave [in Chapel-le-Dale] to the approaches of Hawes there was "nothing but heath over a very fine road, excepting that it is hilly and uphill till we began to descend towards Hawes."

Those who used the old turnpike via Ribblehead — a turnpike authorised by an Act of Parliament in 1751 — appear to have done so with a feeling of trepidation. The area was pockmarked by swallow holes and natural shafts in the limestone, the most famous of which was Batty Wife Hole, which was invariably filled with water.

Littledale, which was to provide the dark limestone for the viaduct.

It was said that Mr and Mrs Batty were ceaselessly bickering, and that Mr Batty was not above hitting his spouse. She left home; he became penitent and arranged to meet her to affect a reconciliation. The appointed meeting place was the pothole. When he did not turn up on time, the woman drowned herself. When he found out what had happened, he took his own life.

Each Wednesday, Gearstones had a market for corn and oatmeal. To it came laden carts from Wensleydale at a time when much of the country produce was carried by packhorses. Others used the green road northwards from High Birkwith to a single-span bridge across Thorns Gill, not far from Gearstones; after enjoying rest and refreshment here, these packhorse men might continue along the Cam High Road to Wensleydale.

The fair for corn ended about 1870, by which time this ''seat of misery'' was swarming with off-duty navvies as the Midland line to Scotland was being constructed. It is said that a Tasmanian called Sharland, who surveyed the route the line must take, was marooned at Gearstones with some of his men, when a blizzard clogged the landscape. The man who must decide where the tunnels of the railway should be placed had to arrange for a tunnel to be made through a snowdrift so that the men could reach a water trough!

Gearstones, with its inn, was the old focal point. Then attention switched to Batty Green, across which the Midland Railway proposed to build a viaduct. The Batty family had already bestowed its name on Batty Wife Hole, the natural shaft that was the setting for a double tragedy. I have already mentioned the drownings. Another story relates that it was named after Mrs Batty simply because she was in the habit of doing the family wash there!

Part of the documentation when the Midland Railway compulsorily purchased land at Ribblehead.

Dated 19th July 1870

Settle to Carlisle Railway No. 1

James Farrer Esquire

to

The Midland Railway Company

Duplicate

Conveyance

of pieces of land & Hereditaments in the Parishes of Horton in Ribblesdale Bentham and Sedbergh in the West Riding of the County of York.

The Events of 1869

Contractor's Locomotive of the 1870s.

THE THRUSTFUL Midland Railway Company, in its northward progress, acquired a lease of the Little North-Western Railway, which joined the Leeds and Bradford Railway at Shipley and ran up the valley to Ingleton. The Ingleton-Tebay line, which might bring the Midland system into contact with the West Coast route to Scotland, was controlled by a rival, The London and North-Western, who had not been very co-operative. Thwarted, the Midland found a way of obtaining access to Carlisle on their own metals, even though it duplicated the West Coast route and would be 24 miles longer.

When the London and North Western realised the Midland would be as good as its word, further negotiations took place and the inter-company bickering between two great companies came to an end with amicable arrangement to share the route. An application was made to Parliament to permit the Act relating to the Settle-Carlisle scheme to be dropped, but Parliament insisted that the work continue.

The Midland thereupon dusted down its plans and set about implementing them. They had in mind a railway to Scotland that would seek to be as good as those of its rivals, to the west and east. There would be shallow curves, permitting fast movement of trains. The ruling gradient in the Pennine area would be 1 in 100, which would test the current state of engineering and in particular the viaduct that would be made where several valleys met at what is now called Ribblehead.

The men who put the work into effect were typically Victorian in their drive and energy. Inspiration was given by James Allport, General Manager of the Midland, who had brought the matter to a head by expressing dismay at the old arrangements with the London and North Western.

Then there was John S. Crossley, the Midland Engineer, who would supervise the construction of the line. He delayed his retirement so that he could see the work through. A third most important figure was John Sharland, a Tasmanian who had surveyed the route the Settle-Carlisle would take and who interested himself in all aspects of the plan until illness forced his retirement to Torquay where, within a short time, he had died.

Sharland was mentioned in F.S. Williams's book on the Midland Railway and nowhere else. In 1976, a small committee planned the celebration of the Settle-Carlisle centenary, and I was carrying out some historical research, when doubts arose that Sharland had existed. Late one evening, the telephone rang at home and an Antipodean voice remarked: "Say, my name's Sharland." He had heard about the celebrations and offered information and a photograph about the great surveyor.

The railway work was let out in four

contracts—one of 17¼ miles from Settle to a point just north of Dent Head; the second of 17 miles to Kirkby Stephen; then one of 15 miles from Kirkby Stephen to Newbiggin and the fourth, of about 24 miles, forward to Carlisle. (A fifth contract was for the branch line extending for six miles to Hawes). About 29 miles of the line lay in Yorkshire, just under 20 in Westmorland and 24 in Cumberland.

In the autumn of 1869, John Ashwell, of Kentish Town, North London, who had successfully tendered for Contract No. 1, began to assemble men and machines at the edge of Batty Green. The Resident Engineer was Edgar O. Ferguson and the construction of the viaduct would be under the management of Charles and Walter Hirst, with a workforce of 60 or more masons and labourers. Mr Davidson was appointed as the Midland's inspector from "Ingleton Road to Dent Head Viaduct."

A four-wheeled caravan brought from London behind a steam engine provided living accommodation of a sort for the engineers who were making the experimental borings for the piers of a viaduct on Batty Moss. Ten men lived in that van. That winter, one man would stand by the van with a bull's eye lantern as a guide to the homecoming men.

Ingleton, the nearest railway station, began to resemble a "boom" town as large quantities of material were unloaded from trains at the station, to be transported by horse and cart up Storrs Brow and through Chapel-le-Dale to Batty Green. In September, 1869, the number of railway wagons passing through Ingleton station was 1,348. (By September, 1873, it would be 10,699 and a year later an impressive 13,830).

A local man complained: "More men ought to be employed in keeping the highways in a proper state of repair . . . After a good shower of rain, the streets and roads are thick puddle . . . Thacking Road, leading to the Storr's limekilns, is so broken up and worn into hollows, it is reported that axle trees are broken and carts in other ways injured. The road through the dale to Ingleton fells was never in so bad a state of repair within the memory of the oldest inhabitant living."

A Carlisle-Leeds passenger train crossing Ribblehead viaduct in 1983.

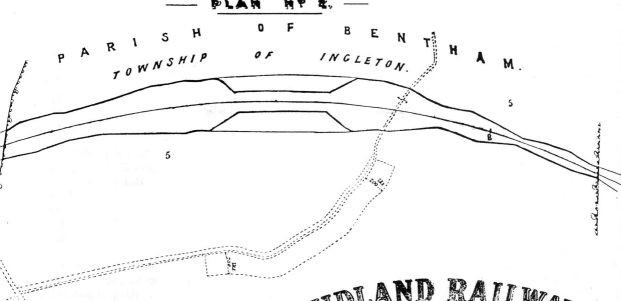

PLAN Nº 2,

PARISH OF BENTHAM.

TOWNSHIP OF INGLETON.

Above — Map showing land at Ribblehead that was purchased from the Farrer family.
Right — A copy of the title page of the Midland Railway (Settle and Carlisle) Land Plan. (See the centre pages for the Ribblehead Viaduct section).
Below — A detailed scale model of the Contractor's Hotel which appeared at Ribblehead in the autumn of 1869. The model was photographed near the famous viaduct.

MIDLAND RAILWAY.
SETTLE & CARLISLE
(SETTLE TO HAWES JUNCTION)
& HAWES BRANCH
LAND PLAN.

Titles of Acts..

That road up Chapel-le-Dale continued to annoy travellers. In 1871, it was reported to have "holes and ridges, ruts and hollows, pools of water and rolling mud." It had become dangerous for carriages, difficult for carting and almost impassable to pedestrians. It would tax the imagination of the poet, the skill of the man of science and the wisdom of a practical road-maker to describe in proper words its broken, miry and wretched condition!

A gentleman who had travelled over the road for more than 50 years remarked that there were not words in the English language to describe its bad state of repair. "I had to scale tottering walls, skip over rushing streams gushing gleesomely from the hillside, and walk over rugged pastures to avoid a road which, for its miserable condition, is almost as widely known as the far-famed Batty Wife Hole."

Everything needed by those who were deputed to build the Ribblehead Viaduct came along this road, for in those days no satisfactorily road existed in the upper valley of the Ribble. From Selside northwards, it would be mainly the creation of the railway company.

At Ribblehead, huge baulks of timber were needed as scaffolding, and one might imagine their passage up Chapel-le-Dale on wagons drawn by several horses. Top priority was given to making a tramway from Batty Green to Blea Moor, where a tunnel was to be made; tramways would also serve the quarry in Littledale and would become numerous in the vicinity of Ribblehead Viaduct.

In June, 1871, a contractor's locomotive was drawn by horses up the Storrs Brow at Ingleton on its way to Mr Ashwell's contract at Batty Wife Hole. "About 3am, the tramp of Mr Ashwell's sleek-skinned and well-fed horses warned many of the people that if they wished to see the removal of the engine from the Back gate, their snug quarters must be quitted without delay," reported the Ingleton correspondent of *The Lancaster Guardian.* "Thirty or more horses were yoked to the locomotive, and they drew it in fine style up the Storrs, which was one of the most difficult ascents in its journey.

"It was fine sight to see so many fine horses willingly exert themselves to draw the ponderous machine. Though the hour of departure was so early, many women as well as men accompanied the lengthy team to above the Storrs. It was well for both man and beast that the weather was so fine, or the imperfect state of the road would have rendered the transit of the engine a difficult matter."

An artist's impression of the transportation by horse power of a Contractor's locomotive from Ingleton to Ribblehead.

Under Construction

One of two photographs of Ribblehead Viaduct in the course of construction. It was photographed from the west. (The other known photograph, of the Viaduct from the east, appears on pages 16 and 17).

A DARK LIMESTONE suitable for the Viaduct was found in Littledale, immediately to the north. It lay on the Ingleborough estate of Mr Farrer—an Estate that extended from Blea Moor over the mountain to Clapham. Old Ingleborough has changed little but photographs of the 1870s show mossland and much heather around Ribblehead. Each summer, the ridges of the mountain were empurpled when the bonnie heather bloomed. Scarcely any heather may be found today.

Ribblehead Viaduct and Blea Moor Tunnel being major undertakings, it was vital to begin the work without delay. The contractor erected huts to accommodate the workmen and their families. The engineers then arranged for shafts to be excavated through peat, clay and washings, to the solid rock at about 25 feet below the surface.

They began at the northern end. Mr Crossley had not at this stage made up his mind how many piers there would be. The Viaduct would be built on a curve of nearly one mile radius and with the ruling gradient 1 in 100. For a time, little appeared to be happening on Batty Green. A contemporary account noted: ''As the foundations of the piers and abutments are laid so deep, a cursory observer will not see the full extent of the progress made.''

When the rock had been bared in a shaft, some six feet of concrete was poured in to provide a durable base for a pier. Masonry was formed of blocks of limestone brought by tramway from Littledale, and as the piers rose, they were enmeshed in a wooden scaffolding, on which light tracks were laid for a steam traveller and the crane that would lift the huge blocks of limestone to where the masons were working. When the masonry reached the height of the gantry, a new ''lift'' of timber was added and the traveller was raised to a new height.

Each of a group of piers terminated at the ''springing'', where the thickness was six feet and the batter on the face 1 inch in 32. The arches were turned and then the scaffolding was dismantled and reassembled to cover a second group of piers, and so on till the work was done.

Photographs of the time show that there was no intrusion on the Ingleton side of the viaduct. A glance at the map shows the reason for this. Here lay the mosses— Gunner Fleet Moss and Low Moss, Parker's

Moss and Bruntscar Moss. East of Batty Moss Viaduct—as it is still named on the Ordnance Survey map—the contractor laid out a spacious workyard and set up the necessary service units—a blacksmith's shop, for the sharpening of implements; a saw mill and carpenter's shed (needed when the scale of the wooden scaffolding is borne in mind); stables for the many horses, a stores—and a pay office.

A network of tramways passed "round the sharpest of curves and up inclines as steep as 1 in 18". The contractor's engine was a "snorting steed"; the tramways were uneven and crooked. The engine went "up and down, heaving on one side and anon on the other, slackening its speed at curves and then accelerating it when they were past; it was enough to make nervous persons giddy enough to relax their hold."

The tramways, which were relatively dry strips on a sodden moor, proved lethal to some who had been drinking at the various inns and beer-houses at Batty Green and were too unsteady to regain their lodgings. They slumped and slept with their heads resting on the rails. The consequence was predictable. For example, in February, 1872, Peter Miles, a mason who had been drinking at the *Railway Inn,* was found dead; he had been run over by a locomotive. The inquest verdict was "accidental death."

Mr Ashwell, the contractor, did much to make the working lives of his masons comfortable. On the gantry, the men had boxes to shelter them from the weather. Sheds were erected on the ground for their comfort when they were off duty.

Above – Within a spandrel on Ribblehead Viaduct.
Below, left – The turning of the first batch of arches
on the Viaduct. Ingleborough lies beyond.
Right – An enlarged detail.

The Workforce

An artist's impression of the laying of the tramway across Batty Moss.

THE 1871 CENSUS for Ingleton Fells new parish recorded an upsurge in the railway population. Eventually, up to 2,000 people were living in a group of shanty-towns between Batty Green and the head of Blea Moor. Of special interest to our story of Ribblehead Viaduct are those whose occupations linked them with such a structure.

John Maud, a mason's labourer from Eathley, boarded with the Bentham family at Winterscale, and in another house the Dowbiggins had two lodgers—William Jackson, a quarryman, and his wife Sarah, who hailed from Sedbergh and Liverpool respectively.

At the shanty-town of Jericho lived William Hughes, a Welshman who was a skilled quarryman. He was head of a household consisting of a wife, three sons, a daughter—and they had four railway labourers as boarders. A Welsh mason, named Joseph Lewis, also of Jericho, had a wife, three sons, a daughter, plus three labourers as boarders.

Sebastopol, a shanty-town close to the Viaduct, was home to Robert and John Nixon, who supervised the brickworks that provided bricks for the Viaduct and Tunnel. Both men and their respective families hailed from Northampton. Robert appears to have had the superior position; he was manager of the Sebastopol brickworks, which were situated near the northern part of the viaduct. (Unhappily for him, his wife eloped with one Henry White. The couple were pursued as far as Skipton, when all trace of them was lost).

Living at Batty Wife, to the south of the turnpike road, were Thomas Worby, a stone mason from Northampton, Abraham Mellor, a stone mason from Halifax, Henry Stone, a carpenter from Misterton in Somerset, and Thomas Bennett, a carpenter from Lambeth. William Mill and Alexander Gordon, two out-of-work stonemasons from Scotland, were at the time of the census boarding with Robert Lodge at Newby Head, on the watershed. This Newby Head, which was then an inn as well as a farmhouse, stands on the watershed at an elevation of 1,400 feet above sea level.

In 1871, the wages at the railway works averaged from 1s. to 1s.6d. per day higher than the wages in Lancashire and Yorkshire. "Many of the masons get 6s.6d. a day." Others worked nine hours a day for only 6s.3d. In summer, the contractor required them to work for 10 hours a day, paying an extra 8d. per hour. In March, 1872, these masons struck. The outcome is not known but presumably they returned to work fairly soon with extra money.

John Ashwell the contractor, got into financial difficulties and was rescued by the Midland. The company decided to put in their own agent rather than invite tenders from other railway contractors. Curiously, the new agent was another Ashwell— William H. Ashwell. He appears to have been

Flying Scotsman comes to a dead halt just before Ribblehead.

A group of Nenthead lead miners give an indication of the type of clothing worn by navvies working on the Settle-Carlisle.

as concerned as his predecessor about the welfare of the men. It was William Ashwell who laid the first stone of the Viaduct, on October 12, 1870.

John Crossley now decided how many arches the Viaduct should have. The number could vary between 18 and 24. Crossley favoured 24. This figure was approved by the Midland's construction committee.

THE VIADUCT BEAUTIFUL: BEYOND IS THE LEONINE FORM OF PENYGHENT.

Stone and Bricks

Left—Aqueduct near Littledale which the Midland built to contain a stream. Littledale was the source of material for the Viaduct.

IN LITTLEDALE, a stream was diverted to expose the finest stone. Ashwell had undertaken a considerable search for a quarry and several trial holes were sunk, the best source being the bed of the stream. The watercourse was diverted. Over 30,000 cubic yards of "black" limestone were removed.

The limestone was dug out in blocks weighing up to four or five tons each. "It is in contemplation to use additional mechanical forces, so that double the number of workmen may be employed. A steam pump will be employed at the quarry; the stone requires much labour to dress it. The class of work is 18-lock in course." At the site of the Viaduct, a 10 h.p. engine was constantly employed for mixing mortar.

"The number of workmen varies much, for though good wages are paid, some of the men generally leave after every pay day; sometimes as many as eight fresh hands are set on the works in a day. According to the opinion of the foreman, it will be two years at the present rate of progress before the viaduct is finished. The work hitherto has been attended with many impeding difficulties, such as the hardness of the stone, the flooding of the quarries by the beck, and the wetness of the moor."

A brick-making machine, made by Porter, Hind and Porter, of Carlisle, was capable of turning out between 18,000 and 20,000 bricks a day. The bricks were needed for the arches of the Viaduct and the Tunnel. They were local bricks. A crushing machine ground up shale, which was then mixed with clay and yielded bricks of such a superior quality that when thrown out of the ovens they "rang like pots". In October, 1871, the brickworks were operating at half capacity. An oven held from 14,000 to 15,000 bricks and it took the workforce of 26 men about a week to fire them.

Some of the "human interest" stories are found in the columns of local newpapers, which reported the proceedings of magistrates' courts and coroner's inquests. In 1871, James Rixon, "brickmaker", was brought before the magistrates at Ingleton charged with assaulting a worker. In

September, 1871, David Davies, aged 32, died while working on the Viaduct. As a three' ton stone was being raised by crane, Davies went under the jib end of the crane; the check-gearing broke off and struck him, fracturing his skull.

An inquest was held at the *Railway Inn,* Batty Green, in April, 1874, on Archibald Matthensen, aged 27, who was described as a railway labourer. He had volunteered to take charge of a horse in the absence of a young man and to draw some wagons laden with stone for Batty Moss Viaduct to the point of decline.

William Jackson, the brakesman, was having a snack. Peter McBride, the ganger, was watching Matthensen. He had drawn one of the immense wagons with over six tons of stone, and had detached the horse from it for its descent, when McBride noticed him lying on the metals about two feet ahead of the descending wagon. He thought he must either have fallen or been knocked down while in the act of uncoupling his horse.

Though McBride shouted to the fallen man to get out of the way, still he appeared to make no effort to do so. Two wheels of the wagon passed over Matthenson's thorax ''and so crushed his heart and lungs that life was destroyed at once.'' The verdict: accidental death.

Digging a cutting.

High Arches

Above – A photograph of Ribblehead from the Riley Collection. In the foreground is the driveway to Ribblehead station, with its fencing in excellent condition.
Below – Tony Freschini, resident engineer, beside the date-stone on Ribblehead viaduct. At the Minister of Transport's request in 1989, British Rail conducted a trial repair of the central pier and arch in order to assess the cost of the repair of the whole viaduct.

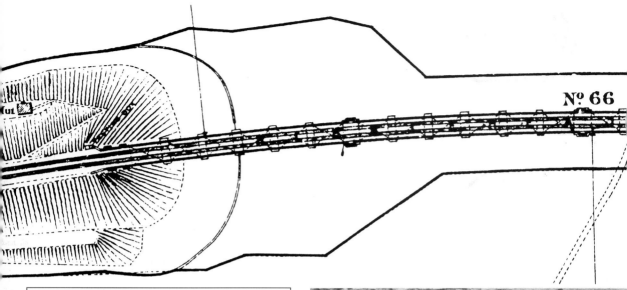

N⁰ 66

Ribblehead
Viaduct from
the air

This splendid photograph was taken by
Simon Pawson from a microlite aircraft.
Notice the many swallow-holes on the moor
and also, at bottom left, what appears to be
the site of the brickworks.

(*Head of page* – The Midland Railway Land
Plan diagram for Midland Railway Bridge
No.66 – Ribblehead Viaduct).

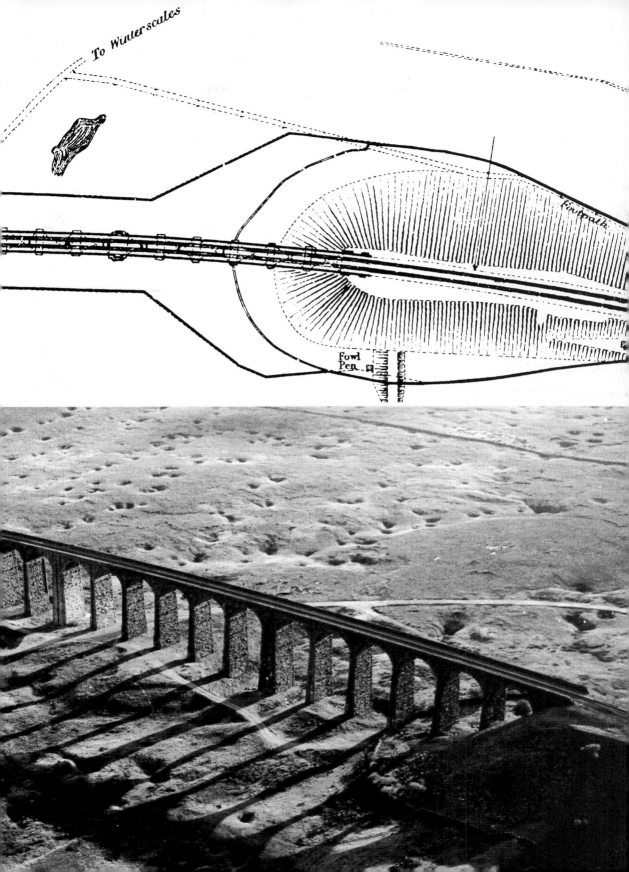

Turning the Arches

A partly built pier on the Settle-Carlisle railway.

IN THE AUTUMN of 1871, the north abutment and the piers for the first six openings were raised to heights varying from 10 feet to 25 feet. The foundations for the next six piers were ready and built up to the level.

In 1872, that first group of six piers were made ready for arching. A year later, 11 of the piers were finished. "The centres are in for six arches and the turning of them in brick began on June 9." Twelve piers were nearly at the top and the rest were at plinth level. In 1873, the first 12 arches were in place, "a tribute to the energy of about 100 men."

Those 12 arches carried brick in the interior and blue limestone quoins. "In fine weather, an arch was finished every week, the first five arches being done in five weeks." Stone was visible, but by the close of the work, a considerable quantity of concrete had been used.

Those who saw the Viaduct remarked on one of its distinctive characteristics—that every sixth pier was a "King Pier", thicker than the average, being 18 feet at the top instead of six. Fine arches between these piers are a continuous structure, so that if one collapses there is nothing to stop the remaining ones folding up—like the proverbial pack of cards. The King Pier is structurally large enough to stop a progressive collapse continuing beyond six arches. Thus a local failure would be limited to six arches.

The Viaduct was "practically finished" by 1875. "The engine and trucks have been running over it for two months, and the parapet walls are now being put on. This work has progressed rapidly during the last 12 months and surprised us when we saw it again. The embankments are also joined up to it on each side, and the large gap is bridged over."

The valley had seemed, about four years before, an almost unsurmountable obstacle, but, noted a contemporary source, "time and perseverance have done great work here. The large arches of 45 feet span each dropped only a quarter of an inch when the centres or supports on which the arch was built were removed. The arches are covered with concrete and then asphalt is laid over to ensure the bricks from getting saturated with water."

Some of the stones of the parapets were of great length. "One of them we measured and found to be 16 feet in length, about 1 foot six inches in width and 1 foot in depth. There is a large stone with 1875 worked on it, being the date of the year the work was finished."

The huge embankments on either side of Ribblehead Viaduct were complete and sown with a ryegrass mixture. On the south side of Batty Green, the Ingleton-road station is in progress. Between Batty Green and Selside, a large number of men were at work making a new road.

There remained the task of laying ballast and fitting rails—82lb steel rails, adapted for heavy traffic and high speeds. On April 29, 1875, a special train conveyed the Midland directors over the whole of the new line "without change of carriage." That August, John Crossley wrote to the construction committee: "I have the pleasure to report that goods trains have this day travelled over the line." It was exactly 10 years from the time he had been authorised to plan the route.

The official first day for goods traffic to begin was August 28. The directors of the Midland Railway promptly recommended a dividend on ordinary stock for the half year at the a rate of 6 per cent per annum. Next year, the passenger service was inaugurated.

The Viaduct stood tall and firm. A visiting newspaperman, much impressed, wrote: "The strong winds blow with a force on this viaduct which is felt on no other viaduct on the line. There will be storms at different seasons in the year when enginemen and stokers will find it necessary to cling to some portions of their engines for support."

The Viaduct and Tunnel Maintenance Train

THIS PHOTOGRAPH, taken in the mid-1970's, shows the train standing on Ribblehead Viaduct, with the towering mass of Whernside beyond. The engineer was using modern hydraulics to move an arm into position so that when occupying a cabin at the end he could closely examine the brickwork under an arch.

In the 1980s, the Minister of Transport (David Mitchell) used this means to inspect one of the arches prior to a debate in the House of Commons on the proposal to close the line.

The train is standing at the place where the Viaduct is at its maximum height of 105 feet. (The height is given in many books as 150 feet). The Viaduct has a length of a quarter of a mile.

At the front and rear of the train are special trucks which used to be pushed by hand through the Tunnels so that men standing on a special platform above could inspect the masonry to see if any of it was "drummy".

Care and Maintenance

WHAT THE TEAM of masons and their men had achieved, generations of railmen sustained. From its moment of opening, the Viaduct, in common with other structures on the Settle-Carlisle, needed care and maintenance. Harry Cox, who was 92 when I interviewed him in 1976, told me he had begun work on the railway in 1904.

It was in the spring of the year, a time when the Midland Railway took on extra men for re-laying track. Between 30 and 40 extra men were needed; he joined the gang, but left when someone was needed to work with the masons who, between 1905 and 1910, re-bricked the most northerly eight arches of the Viaduct.

At that time, a mason had a wage of £1 a week, which was fractionally more than that received by platelayers. Harry was among those who had to lodge-out in summer, a shilling a night being allowed for lodgings. "We took a week's grub with us in tin boxes and found lodgings in the area where we worked. I lodged at Colt Park Farm."

Harry described to me the process that was followed when re-bricking took place "underneath the arches". Bent rails known as "car-heads", were fitted under the track and extended just over the parapet, at which end a ring was fitted. To this ring were attached blocks and tackle to haul into position the heavy baulks needed for the framework of the "floors" or platforms on which the men would work, some 60 feet above the ground. The baulks rested on corbels on the Viaduct piers.

Three floors were required. Harry recalled that scaffolding two arches took about six weeks and attending to the brickwork was spread over three to four weeks. Harry Cox helped to re-brick 10 arches in all, which meant that he worked on Ribblehead Viaduct for several summers. "In amonghands, in winter, we worked in Blea Moor Tunnel," he added.

Jack Towler, who was 89 years of age when I chatted with him in the summer of 1989, began work on Ribblehead Viaduct in 1924. He became a ganger in 1939. "You could feel it trembling in certain places when trains were coming over. Frost used to lift the lines up a bit, especially at the southern end."

For re-laying work, several gangs were brought together. The work was done by hand. "We'd gangs o'men to pick rails up for loading on to wagins. Then they had to pick 'chaired' sleepers up, six men to the sleeper. today it's all done by machinery.''

Jack mentioned some of the special duties in this highland situation. At times of fog, men with warning detonators were summoned; they were provided with huts, two at the north side of the Viaduct, for the ''up'' and ''down'', and one towards Selside.

Ribblehead is notorious for the strength of the wind when a westerly is ramaging across the country. Jack mentioned to me one of the hoary stories of Ribblehead—that the wind plucked the cap from the head of a man who was walking across the Viaduct. The wind took the cap under an arch and up the other side, returning it to his head. ''That's all nothing,'' said Jack. ''I've never seen it.''

A variation of the story relates to Old George, a ganger, who was crossing the Viaduct on a gusty day when the wind blew the cap from his head, under one of the arches and back on to his head. It landed the wrong way round. George said: 'Thou can't have ivverything.'

Cockerill, the ganger, used to tell the tale about being on the Viaduct when a goods train was passing, with a sheet [tarpaulin cover] hanging, and of how a rope wrapped itself round his neck. He had the presence of mind to reach into his pocket for a knife and cut the rope or he would have been strangled. ''That's also nothing.''

The parapets of Ribblehead Viaduct are so high that a westerly gale passes over the head of any railwayman who is crossing. ''On a right wet day, you could go on that viaduct and it would be dry. After coming up the valley, the rain would be driven high over the top.

''The wildest part is the bank between Ribblehead station and the Viaduct. It used to blow sheets galore. During t'war they were all tied up wi' bits o'string and all sorts of stuff that wasn't good enough. The wind soon broke 'em.''

60009 Union of South Africa crosses Ribblehead viaduct on July 23, 1984.

The flying tarpaulin was a hazard peculiar to Ribblehead. "No sheets came off wagins on t'Viaduct. They blew down into t'bottom of t'banks. We had 'em to collect, fold up and put on a bogey to be carted to the station. I've had as many as 100 sheets to pick up. The wind was sometimes strong enough to stop a train and a small locomotive had to be brought up behind to shove them out."

The trains most likely to be beaten to a halt were those with cattle wagons. I heard from one frustrated driver that "we were going to Hawes for cattle and had 35 empty cattle wagons on. We had a No. 3 freight. At Ribblehead Viaduct, it blew us to a stand. The guard had to come and divide us, so we could take a few wagons through at a time."

On the night a gale blew cars off some transporter trucks at Ribblehead Viaduct, a Garsdale ganger, Mr Harper, was roused by Ted Ashton, the signalman, shouting up to say that some cars were lying in Blea Moor Tunnel. There was a train on the "up" road and Ted had stopped it. The train gave the ganger a lift to Blea Moor and dropped him at the north end of the tunnel; he walked through but saw no cars.

The photograph (above), which appears to have been taken about the turn of the century, shows a Midland 4-4-0 locomotive hauling a rake of clerestoried coaches south off Ribblehead Viaduct.
On close inspection, it seems that one of the crew is sitting on the "splasher" [the large cover over the driving wheel] in front of the cab, a hair-raising practice that was sometimes undertaken by the enginemen to escape high winds in the cab.
The telegraph poles are no longer in existence. Wires were to be laid at ground level.

He phoned from the end of the tunnel and the driver brought the train slowly through. The man walked on to the Viaduct. About six cars lay on their bonnets on the "up" road. "It was a wild night. A freak gust of wind must have lifted them off. They were not normally fastened down."

In recent times, snow blocked the Settle-Carlisle for long periods in 1947 and 1963. The snow-bearing winds came from the north-east. One of the problems was the continuing wind which, after a day of labour to clear the track, blew the snow back into the excavations. On occasions, snow was thrown over viaducts like Ribblehead to dispose of it.

The cutting between the Viaduct and Blea Moor was soon filled with snow. "They never seemed to mention this; it was always Dent that was blocked!" In 1947, prisoners of war were brought up in ballast trains to clear snow out of Ribblehead station; the snow was emptied over the parapets of the Viaduct.

"I remember one lot of prisoners arriving. They wouldn't get out of the train to clear snow. When eventually the inspector got them out and got the wagons filled and took them to t'Viaduct, they wouldn't empty t'wagons. That inspector was a very religious man; and they 'turned' him. I never heard a man swear as much in all my life! He said: 'If my wife could hear me now, she'd drop down dead!'"

Jack worked 12 hours a day, "and when he came home at night," said his wife, "he went straight into the kitchen, took his coat off, and it stood up by itself! He was off work with frost-bitten nose and ears after that."

During the 1939-45, the Home Guard defended the Viaduct against possible enemy action. A few men with one gun and several rounds of ammunition went through the ritual of attending at night. It is recalled that at the end of the spell of duty, a check had to be made that there was no ammunition "up the spout" of the gun. One man, believing the gun was clear, pulled the trigger and a bullet went through the ceiling of Ribblehead waiting room and shattered a roof tile.

In wartime, the derailment of trucks was not uncommon. Two ammunition wagons came off at Ribblehead box. "They'd jumped t'line. We'd to get troops to come and move 'em." Enemy aircraft quested for Ribblehead or Dentdale viaducts. Alf Flack reported going out one night and watching flares descending near the Viaduct.

Jack and his men were crossing the Viaduct on one misty evening when they heard a large aircraft coming. "I said: 'He'll

Contractor's men engaged in water proofing the viaduct.
Note the lighting system. This was provided so that work was possible through the night.

An artist's impression of a M.R. small locomotive, of a type that was often used to assist trains over Ribblehead in gale force winds.

have to look out, the way he's going.' We didn't get much further before there was such a bang. A Wellington bomber had crashed into Whernside.''

In 1978, after 10 steamless years on the Settle-Carlisle, the steam special returned; in 1980, it had a name, the Cumbrian Mountain Express. Early in 1981, a report indicated that Ribblehead Viaduct was deteriorating to such an extent that it would either have to be replaced within as little as five years or the line closed.

A figure of £6m was mentioned. Ribblehead Viaduct was publicised so much that, on the one hand, the state of its fabric became a major argument for closure and, on the other hand, the Viaduct came to represent the invincible Settle-Carlisle for those who were fighting to keep it open!

Rain, not the notorious wind, was causing the major damage to Ribblehead Viaduct. The average rainfall is about 70 inches,

though in 1954 the total was over 100 inches, five of which fell on a single December day. The century-old drainage system involves hollow spandrels—those triangular pieces at the head of the piers—and iron downspouts. Water seeped in the wrong places, through cracks in slate and layers of asphalt that had deteriorated. Water finding its water into the heads of the piers mixed with the ''fill''—the mortar and rubble—reducing this to a sort of clayey mud. The water eventually trickled through the outer skin from dozens of cracks between the squared limestone, having washed away the mortar.

Lime used for the original mortar was ''hydraulic'', brought from Barrow near Leicester. The mixture with local sand had not been satisfactory, and by the early 1980s could be raked out when dry, being washed away by escaping water during periods of heavy rain.

An Artist's Impressions

The railway engineers naturally tried to arrest the water-damage at source, by attending to the drainage high above the ground. One of the slabs of "slate"—the local type, known as Horton Flags—was removed and a manhole cover fitted to enable men to explore and examine the spandrel-voids.

Finding heavy iron downspouts was not easy, and substituted material was used with varying success. Asbestos lasted for a few years but the plastic down-spouting tended to be blown from its clamps. The "black" limestone of Littledale, of which the viaduct was built, is always of variable quality. Some stones are very weak ("shaley") and have severely weathered. With limestone, "point load" also causes failure of the stone.

I studied a section of a block of limestone that had fallen some 70 feet from the top of a pier. The friable nature could be seen in a hundred places. There was cracking and "shelling", each an invitation to the frost to penetrate and cause further damage.

Ribblehead Viaduct, with its bracing made from old railway tracking and, later, from concrete casing, looked like an ailing giant in splints. Individual stones had been secured using bolts and cartridges. The latter, made of mortar in a plastic skin, were known to the railway workers as "sausages".

A 30 mile an hour speed restriction was in force, and yet the viaduct built for Kirtley locomotives and their modest strings of carriages or wagons had been used for many years by trains weighing 900 and more tons.

A memorial to the workmen, past and present, who created and restored the viaduct.

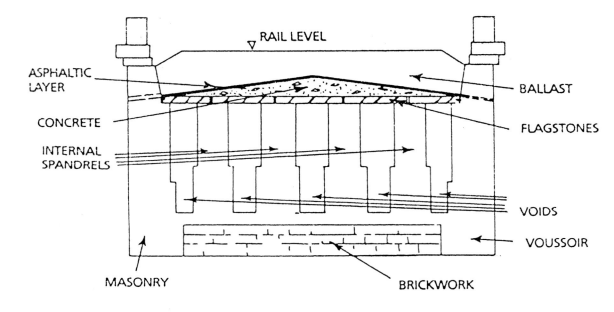

ASPHALTIC LAYER

CONCRETE

INTERNAL SPANDRELS

MASONRY

RAIL LEVEL

BALLAST

FLAGSTONES

VOIDS

VOUSSOIR

BRICKWORK

CROSS SECTION OF EXISTING DECK

Fig 1

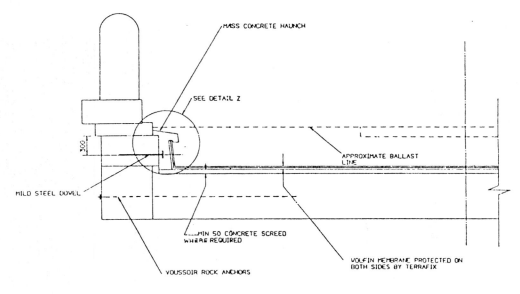

MASS CONCRETE HAUNCH

SEE DETAIL Z

300

MILD STEEL DOWEL

MIN 50 CONCRETE SCREED WHERE REQUIRED

VOUSSOIR ROCK ANCHORS

APPROXIMATE BALLAST LINE

VOLFIN MEMBRANE PROTECTED ON BOTH SIDES BY TERRAFIX

HALF SECTION A—A

CROSS SECTION OF NEW DECK

Fig 2

It had excessive use in two world wars.

The period of most rapid decline was from the 1950s to the 1980s. The last steam train under the old regime used the Drag on August 11, 1968. Henceforth, we saw faceless diesel locomotives, though we have now grown quite attached to their special qualities! Half a million pounds were spent on Ribblehead Viaduct during the 1970s.

British Rail began to divert traffic from the line, presumably to support its case for closure. BR proposed to sell it off, but the Friends of the Settle-Carlisle objected strongly and put forward such a good case that, a decade later, BR was told by the Transport Minister that they must continue to run the line. It is to their credit that they have since tackled the project with enthusiasm and some hard cash.

For two weeks, in the autumn of 1989, the line was closed. The deck of Ribblehead Viaduct was waterproofed. Before any work could be started, the rails had to be lifted and 2,500 tonnes of ballast removed. Once the deck had been exposed, this was cleaned and all faults repaired.

At the same time, the parapet walls were strengthened with concrete, which in addition to providing a clean line to work to, enabled the waterproof membrane to be

Contractor's men, looking like spacemen in their waterproof garments, pause briefly before carpeting Ribblehead viaduct with the Terrafix underfelt. This was used to protect the waterproof membrane, which stops seepage of rainwater into the piers. About 2,500 tons of fresh ballast were brought from North Wales. The Terrafix protected the membrane from the granite chippings.

keyed-in, giving a total seal. Next came the laying of the waterproof membrane, a layer of Wolfing IB, on "Terrafix", which is not unlike very thick carpet felt. Another layer of "Terrafix" was placed on top. This protected the membrane from damage by the ballast, which was then replaced and the track re-laid.

The work had been put out to contract. One worker remarked, grimly: "One of these days, they'll shock us and let us do it in summer, when the weather's decent." A few men and a few ultra-powerful machines set about the work. I saw a crane with a boom capable of extending from the ground to well above the level of the parapets, and a "concrete pump", an ingenious vehicle which, having received ready-mixed concrete from another vehicle extended a pipe until it was at parapet level, 100 feet above, and then proceeded to pump up the concrete, which, by means of movements of the vehicle and a flexible nozzle, could be poured precisely where it was needed.

Night was made as day by powerful arc lights to enable the men to work in shifts throughout 24 hours. On the first of three Sundays, tracked vehicles with scoops worked on the viaduct, shifting the old ballast (which was simply dumped over the side). On the third Sunday, the tracks were being relayed by British Rail workers. A mobile crane attached to a diesel locomotive lifted lengths of track from their prescribed positions and moved them to where the platelayers awaited them.

As wind-blown rain made everyone's life a misery, I took sanctuary in a brake van near Ribblehead station. The railwaymen worked on, in the spirit of the Settle-Carlisle.

Commemorative photographs mark the completion of a general restoration.
Left to right – Tony Freschini, Geoff Bounds and the author.

Re-Opened for Business

RE-OPENING SHORTLY. FOR A LONG, LONG TIME.

On Monday 30th October after two weeks of extensive renovation, the magnificent Ribblehead Viaduct will once again be open.

As well as the viaduct itself, we've carried out major work on three bridges along the route between Settle and Appleby, at a cost of over half a million pounds.

We believe it's money well spent. For the Settle-Carlisle line not only provides a vital link for many local people, it passes through some of England's most spectacular countryside.

And as the line's future is now assured for many years to come, we hope you'll be among the thousands of people from all over the country who enjoy this wonderful journey.

Right — B.R. used extensive advertising to inform passengers of the closure of Ribblehead Viaduct for a fortnight in 1989. This simple and stark advertisement which announced the re-opening also publicises the railway.

Below — A specially invited group from the media being shown the completed work on Ribblehead Viaduct on the day on which traffic was resumed.

A drawing of one of the Settle-Carlisle viaducts during construction (from F.S. Williams's book "The Midland Railway").

Above – A drawing from the pen of Rowland Lindup. Horse-drawn transport on the special tramway at Ribblehead. *Below* – The bustling life at Batty Green is imaginatively recaptured. The picture is one of a series by Betty Harrington.

THE ARCHES IN FINE DETAIL. SEVERAL ARCHES WERE BUILT OF DOUBLE THICKNESS.

Ribblehead in the Snow

Above—Ribblehead Viaduct in the bleak midwinter. Below—This photograph from the Weston Collection was specially posed at Ribblehead on December 28, 1906. The locomotives are Class 2F 0-6-0s with a riding van sandwiched between them.

Above – Ribblehead in the winter of 1986.
Below – Southern Railway No.777 hauls a special from Leeds to Carlisle on a sharp winter's day.

What They Said About Ribblehead Viaduct

SEEN from the inside of the curve, Ribblehead viaduct is magnificent. Below, adjoining the Ingleton to Hawes road, and under and alongside the viaduct, there is a pitted barren stretch of open moorland where nothing grows save rough grass and nothing lives save a few wild creatures . . .

Peter E. Baughan, in "North of Leeds"
(1966)

There is no other viaduct quite like Ribblehead. A quarter of a mile long and built on a gentle yet majestic curve, its 24 arches soar 105 feet above the surrounding moorland. Yet it is set in such a vast landscape of high mountains that it is dwarfed to the extent of looking almost like a model, with the trains as mere specks against a backdrop of bleak and barren hills.

David Joy, "Settle-Carlisle in Colour"
(1983)

Railwaymen tell many anecdotes about the severity of the weather on Ribblehead viaduct and the one which relates how a man was blown off the viaduct, through an arch, and back on to the viaduct, is typical if not authentic. Trains of cattle wagons are particularly vulnerable to the gales since cattle wagons are open, under the roof, to the wind. Many a driver when taking such a load over the exposed stretches of the line has felt that alarming shuddering jerk or drag which tells him that the wind is at odds with his own desires.

Frederick W. Houghton and
W. Hubert Foster (1948)

Ribblehead viaduct is very famous for its winds. I've even seen cars blown over the side. We had several wagons loaded with them one wild night a few years back; halfway over the viaduct, there was a sudden terrific shower of sparks. When we got to Dent box, the signalman shouted: "Lads! Three of them Humber Snipes is missing!" And, by heck, they were. We found them at first light—just scrap metal down in the stream bed.

A Guard on the Long Drag

The viaduct is a scheduled Ancient Monument, and fully deserves to be properly repaired. It looks impressive as you see it from the train, but the sheer scale of the civil engineering only becomes fully apparent as you stand underneath it. Viewed from the valley floor, it is an awesome feeling to think that it was built by men with virtually no mechanical equipment.

P.M. Shaw in "Settle & Carlisle Sunset"
(1988)

Above – A Class 40 Diesel heading a long train of mixed traffic northwards in the mid-1970s.
Below – Photograph of the scaffolding in 1989.

Night work on Ribblehead, 1989. A photograph by Graham Lindley ("The Yorkshire Post").

A Postscript...

RIBBLEHEAD VIADUCT epitomises the spirit of a railway that was laid in a wild countryside at enormous cost in men and money. I have seen the Viaduct hundreds of times—and each time it has looked different from all previous occasions. Limestone, especially when wet, takes on the tones round about. Ribblehead is most appealing when tinted by the reds of a winter sunset.

The Viaduct is now scheduled as an Ancient Monument—a Monument that is still in daily use!

An engineer remarked: "You have to take your hat off to the men who built Ribblehead Viaduct. When you consider the primitive equipment they had, it is a fantastic piece of engineering work."

O.S. Nock, who first thrilled to the Settle-Carlisle when he was a boy at Giggleswick School in 1916, has written: "Nowhere else in the world have my railway interests and my love of wild mountain country been more thoroughly and happily integrated."